G000061795

The Last Juror

John Grisham

Level 2

Retold by Annette Keen
Series Editors: Andy Hopkins and Jocelyn Potter

Pearson Education Limited

Edinburgh Gate, Harlow,
Essex CM20 2JE, England
and Associated Companies throughout the world.

ISBN: 978-1-4082-6119-4

This edition first published by Pearson Education Ltd 2011

5 7 9 10 8 6

Original copyright © John Grisham, 2004
Text copyright © Pearson Education Ltd 2011

Illustrations by Paul Davidson

The moral rights of the authors have been asserted in accordance with
the Copyright Designs and Patents Act 1988

Set in 12/15.5pt A. Garamond
Printed in China
SWTC/05

Published by Pearson Education Ltd

Acknowledgements

The publisher would like to thank the following for their kind permission
to reproduce their photographs:

(Key: b-bottom; c-centre; l-left; r-right; t-top)

Corbis: 58t, 58b; i**Stockphoto**: Brytta 59tl, roccomontoya 59b; **Thinkstock**: iStockphoto 59tr

*Every effort has been made to trace the copyright holders and we apologise in advance for any unintentional omissions.
We would be pleased to insert the appropriate acknowledgement in any subsequent edition of this publication.*

For a complete list of the titles available in the Pearson English Active Readers series, visit www.pearsonenglishactivereaders.com.
Alternatively, write to your local Pearson Education office or to
Pearson English Readers Marketing Department, Pearson Education, Edinburgh Gate, Harlow, Essex CM20 2JE, England.

Contents

1.1 What's the book about?

Talk to another student.

1 Do you know any of John Grisham's books, or any of the movies from his books? What kind of stories does he write?

2 Read the first four lines of Chapter 1. What do you think this story is about?

3 What picture do you have of small towns in the south of the United States? Discuss the houses and the stores, the people and their lives.

1.2 What happens first?

Look at this picture. What do you think? Circle the best word in each sentence.

1 The man looks *happy / afraid / angry*.

2 He is in his *house / office / store*.

3 The gun is *his / a friend's / a killer's*.

4 He is planning to *fight / kill / talk to* somebody.

CHAPTER 1

A Very Big Story

*"The Padgitts have a lot of money. They can buy people, or
hurt people. They will want to help Danny. So be careful."*

Ford **County** in Mississippi isn't the most exciting place in the United
States. Not much happens in Clanton, the small town at the center
of Ford County. Most of the time it's quiet and people live there without
any big problems. Most of the time …

But in March 1970, something did happen in Clanton. There was a
murder. You don't forget a murder. Thirty years later, I can remember
everything about that day. My name is Willie Traynor, and in 1970 I was
the **editor** of the Ford County newspaper, the *Times*. I talked to the dead
woman's sister and her neighbors. I talked to the **lawyers** and the police. I
wrote the story for the *Times*, and some weeks later I sat through the **trial**.
And I was a friend of one of the **jurors**.

Rhoda Kassellaw was the dead woman. She met her killer in a bar.
They talked and then they danced. But when the man wanted more, she
pushed him away. He was very angry. Rhoda left the bar and he followed
her home. He saw the light in her bedroom, and he quietly went in the
back door. Rhoda's killer had a knife and he cut her many times.

Rhoda's neighbor, Mr. Deece, found her. Before she died, she spoke to
him. "Danny Padgitt," she said. "It was Danny Padgitt." Those were her
last words. Mr. Deece called the hospital and the police, but it was too
late for Rhoda.

county /ˈkaʊnti/ (n) Each *county* in the state of Mississippi has a number of towns in it.
murder /ˈmɜːdə/ (n/v) A killing is *murder* when the killer wanted to kill the dead person. It
was not an accident.
editor /edətə/ (n) The *editor* is the top man (or woman) in a newspaper office.
lawyer /ˈlɔjə/ (n) When you have a problem with the police, a *lawyer* can help you. Lawyers
understand the *laws* of a country better than other people.
trial /ˈtraɪəl/ (n) After the police catch somebody, there is often a *trial*. Then that person is
free again—or not.
juror /ˈdʒuːrə/ (n) At important trials there are twelve men and women *jurors*.

Danny Padgitt drove away from Rhoda's house as fast as he could. But it was dark and Danny was afraid. He didn't drive carefully. When an animal ran across the road in front of him, his car left the road. It turned over, then hit a tree. Danny climbed out through a window. Then he saw the blue lights of a police car.

Danny Padgitt lived outside Clanton, near the Big Brown River, with his family. The Padgitts were a bad family and they usually stayed away from the town. The people of Clanton stayed away from them, too. The Padgitts had a lot of money, but nobody knew how, or how much. "It's dirty money," people said. "The Padgitts hurt people. They killed for their money."

I heard a lot of stories about the Padgitts when I came to Clanton. They were all bad stories. But I never met any of the family.

I heard about Danny Padgitt at about midnight and I went quickly to the town **jail**. There were a lot of policemen outside the jail. A police

jail /dʒeɪl/ (n) When people do something very bad, they go to *jail*.

2

car arrived and Danny Padgitt got out. There was **blood** on his clothes. I started to think about my story for the newspaper.

Sheriff Coley came out of the jail and I pushed through the policemen.

"Sheriff, can you answer some questions, please? What can you tell me about the murder?" I asked him.

"A white woman, age thirty-one," he said.

"Did you **arrest** anybody?" I asked.

"Yes, we arrested a man, but I can't give you his name now. Ask me again in two or three hours."

"Danny Padgitt?"

"I can't say, Mr. Traynor."

I left the jail and drove to Rhoda's house. There were police cars outside, and some of her neighbors.

"I think Rhoda had a boyfriend," one man told me. "He's a lawyer in town." But he didn't know the man's name.

I asked some other neighbors about Rhoda, but she lived quietly. Most people didn't know much about her.

I wrote my story for the front page of the newspaper. Next to it, I put a picture of Danny Padgitt outside the jail. He was between two policemen. We sold a lot of newspapers that week.

The people of Clanton talked about the Kassellaw murder in every **café** and bar in town. They also talked about it at their dinner tables in many Clanton homes. Callie Ruffin's home was one of them.

Every Thursday I had lunch at the house of Esau and Callie Ruffin. In 1970, black people and white people didn't live on the same streets. In Clanton, black people lived in Lowtown. This was across town from my house. The Ruffin house was in Lowtown.

I first met Callie Ruffin when I wrote a story about her family. Everybody in Clanton called her Miss Callie. She had eight children, and

---

blood /blʌd/ (n) When you cut your finger, red *blood* runs out.
sheriff /ˈʃerɪf/ (n) The *sheriff* is the most important policeman in an American town.
arrest /əˈrest/ (v) When you do something very wrong, the police will *arrest* you.
café /ˈkæfeɪ/ (n) You can usually eat quickly and for little money in a *café*.

seven of them were college teachers. Her youngest son, Sam, was the first black child at the white school in Clanton. The children didn't live in Ford County now—only Esau and Miss Callie were left in the house in Lowtown.

Miss Callie liked to cook and I liked to eat. So every Thursday, she invited me to lunch. The vegetables came from their yard and she was a wonderful cook. Sometimes Esau ate with us, but usually it was Miss Callie and me.

She always read every page of the *Times*, and she found every little mistake in it. "There's an 'a' in 'theater';" or "You used the wrong word there, Mr. Traynor." It was four years before she called me Willie.

The Thursday after the murder, Miss Callie and I talked about it. She felt sad for Rhoda Kassellaw's family.

"In fifty years I don't remember a worse thing in Clanton," she said. "Aren't you afraid of the Padgitts? Your story on the front page of the newspaper was very bad for Danny."

"I'm only doing my job," I said. "I write the **truth**."

"The Padgitts have a lot of money. They can buy people, or hurt people. They will want to help Danny. So be careful."

"I'll be careful," I said.

But I didn't think about our conversation again that day.

The next morning, a man arrived at my office and put a gun down on my desk. I knew his face, but not his name.

"I'm Harry Rex Vonner," he said. "Do you have a gun? You can have this one."

I was a city boy from Memphis. I didn't know anything about guns, but I was afraid of them.

"It's a Smith and Wesson .38," said Harry Rex. "A good gun. Can you use it?"

"I don't think I can," I said.

"Come to my house this evening and I'll show you. I know these

truth /truːθ/ (n) When your story is right, you are telling the *truth*.

4

Padgitts—they're a dangerous family. And they won't like you very much now."

Harry Rex was a lawyer in Clanton. He taught me about the gun and he taught me a lot about the Padgitts. After this, I carried the Smith and Wesson with me every day. But it was too big for my jacket, so I started to leave it in the car. Then, after two or three weeks, I forgot about it.

The town was quiet again. The Padgitts didn't come into Clanton, and we heard nothing about them. It was summer and it was hot. People didn't forget about the trial, but they stopped talking about it all the time. The town waited. And in Clanton's jail, Danny Padgitt waited, too.

CHAPTER 2

The Padgitt Trial

"Don't send me to jail or you'll be sorry," Danny said, angrily.
"I'll find you. And I'll kill all of you!"

The lawyer for the State was Ernie Gaddis. Danny Padgitt's lawyer was Lucien Wilbanks. He was not a nice man. But the most important people at the trial were the jurors—twelve men and women from Ford County. Was Danny Padgitt **guilty** of murder? They had to find the answer.

Callie Ruffin was one of the jurors. She was the first black woman juror in Ford County. She was excited, but a little afraid.

"How will I know the truth about Danny Padgitt?" she asked me one Thursday lunchtime.

"You listen carefully to the lawyers. Then you discuss it with the other jurors. You'll know, Miss Callie."

guilty /ˈɡɪlti/ (adj) When you do something bad, you are *guilty* of that.

"And the **death penalty**? Who says that a guilty man has to die?"
"The jurors."
"Oh, no. I don't think I can do that."
Miss Callie didn't want her lunch after that. She was very quiet.

◆

Danny Padgitt's trial started in June. I looked around the **courtroom** on the first day. The Padgitt family were there, near Lucien Wilbanks. Ernie Gaddis was there with another man.

"Who's that man?" I asked Harry Rex quietly.

"Hank Hooten," he said. "He works with Ernie. He was Rhoda's boyfriend for a time, but Ernie doesn't know that."

Hank Hooten was about forty years old, with gray hair. He sat behind Ernie, and sometimes Ernie spoke to him.

The jurors came into the courtroom. I only knew Miss Callie. Harry Rex knew seven of them.

"Maybe the Padgitts will buy some of them. They have the money."

"Not Miss Callie," I said. "They'll never buy her. She's a very strong woman."

One of the young men couldn't walk very well.

"His name's Lenny Fargarson," said Harry Rex. "And that man in the yellow shirt is Mo Teale. He works with farm machines."

The trial started. Ernie Gaddis spoke first and called some **witnesses**. The jurors looked at photos of the dead woman. They heard from policemen and doctors. Sheriff Coley spoke, then Rhoda's sister.

At the end of the first day, the jurors drove away from Clanton. They stayed in a hotel in another town. Nobody knew where. I went back to my office and wrote the story for the newspaper.

The trial started again the next day. The courtroom was full again. This time, Lucien Wilbanks spoke first.

death penalty /deθ ˈpenlti/ (n) Some countries kill murderers after their trial. These countries have the *death penalty*.
courtroom /ˈcɔrtrum/ (n) A trial happens in a *courtroom*. Courtrooms are in a courthouse.
witness /ˈwɪtnəs/ (n) A *witness* sees something or knows something important. At a trial, *witnesses* have to speak in the courtroom

"Danny Padgitt is not guilty of this murder," he began. "He was with somebody that night before his car accident. A girlfriend."

The jurors listened carefully. The girlfriend came into the courtroom and answered a lot of questions. But Ernie Gaddis also questioned her. He was smart and she couldn't answer every question.

"She's not telling the truth," Harry Rex said to me quietly. "Look at her face. I think the Padgitts paid her."

More witnesses came into the courtroom. Ernie Gaddis and Lucien Wilbanks asked them questions. One of the witnesses was Rhoda's neighbor, Mr. Deece. He remembered everything about the night of the murder.

"Did she say anything?" Ernie asked him.

"She said, 'It was Danny Padgitt'," said Mr. Deece. "And then she died."

Some of the jurors looked at Danny Padgitt. One of the women started to cry.

Danny Padgitt spoke next. The courtroom was very quiet. He walked to the witness box and smiled at the jurors.

"I want these good people to hear the truth," said Danny. "I'm not the killer." He told them his story, but it wasn't the truth. Everybody knew that now. And Danny stopped smiling when Ernie Gaddis asked him questions.

"What did you do with the knife?" Ernie asked.

"I wasn't there," said Danny, but he looked very guilty.

"Then why was there blood on your clothes? I think you were there. I think you killed Rhoda Kassellaw that night. You drove away from her house …"

"I didn't do it!" Danny shouted.

"No more questions," said Ernie, and he sat down.

Danny walked away from the witness box slowly. He looked angry and afraid. Then he suddenly turned to the jurors.

"Don't send me to jail or you'll be sorry," he said angrily. "I'll find you. And I'll kill all of you!"

A policeman took Danny out of the courtroom. There was a lot of noise in the room. Some of the Padgitt family shouted angrily at Ernie. Everybody was talking at the same time. Only the jurors were quiet. They looked afraid.

After lunch, we listened to the lawyers' last words. Then the jurors left the room. Everybody waited.

When the jurors came in again, one of them stood up.

"Danny Padgitt is guilty of murder," he said. "But we are not asking for the death penalty."

Danny went to jail for life. He didn't die, because one or more of the jurors didn't want the death penalty. The people of Clanton were very angry about this.

2.1 Were you right?

Look back at your answers to Activity 1.2 on page iv. Then look at this picture. Are these sentences right (✓) or wrong (✗)?

1 ⬭ Harry Rex is giving the gun to Willie.

2 ⬭ He wants to help Willie.

3 ⬭ The two men are in Willie's home.

4 ⬭ Willie knows nothing about guns.

5 ⬭ After this, Willie always carries the gun.

2.2 What more did you learn?

Put the right name in each sentence.

| Hank Hooten | Callie Ruffin | Rhoda Kassellaw | Ernie Gaddis |
| Danny Padgitt | Lucien Wilbanks | Willie Traynor | Mr. Deece |

1 The dead woman is ....

2 .... was her neighbor.

3 Her killer's name is ....

4 .... is the editor of the *Times* newspaper.

5 He has lunch every Thursday with ....

6 Danny Padgitt's lawyer is ....

7 .... and .... work for the State.

2.3 Language in use

Read the sentences in the box.
Then finish these sentences in the
same way.

> He **quietly** went in the back door.
>
> The jurors listened **carefully**.

1 Danny drove ....*dangerously*........ . (dangerous)

2 Willie went .... to the jail. (quick)

3 Miss Callie talked .... about Rhoda's family. (sad)

4 Lucien Wilbanks spoke very .... (loud)

5 Danny spoke .... to the jurors. (angry)

6 One of the jurors couldn't walk very .... (good)

2.4 What happens next?

Discuss these questions. Which of these people do you think is going to
use a gun in the next chapter? Why?

Willie Traynor

Harry Rex Vonner

Hank Hooten

Lucien Wilbanks

Danny Padgitt

Another person

CHAPTER 3

More Guns, More Blood

"Padgitt's in jail for life," said her son Bobby.
"And that's good. He can't hurt anybody now."

E verybody in Clanton talked about the Padgitt trial for days after it
ended. A lot of people wrote letters to the newspaper. I went to
lunch with Miss Callie on the first Thursday after the trial.

"We didn't do a good job, Mr. Traynor," she said. "Everybody is
saying that. They wanted the death penalty for Danny Padgitt." She said
nothing more about the trial. Some of the jurors didn't want the death
penalty, but nobody knew who. "We will never tell," she said.

Some of Miss Callie's children were at the house.

"Padgitt's in jail for life," said her son Bobby. "And that's good. He
can't hurt anybody now."

But I knew better. Harry Rex told me about the law in Mississippi. It
wasn't the same as the law in other states.

"Here, 'life' means ten years," Harry Rex said.

"But that's crazy," I said. "So Danny Padgitt will be out of jail after
ten years?"

"Maybe before that. I know it's stupid, but it's the law, Willie."

"Did the jurors know this?"

"No, and Ernie couldn't tell them. That's Mississippi law, too. And
yes, it's crazy."

I didn't tell Miss Callie, or her family.

◆

By the end of September, most conversations in Clanton were about other
things. There were some big football games and it was a busy time for
the farmers of Ford County. Slowly, people forgot about the Padgitts.

But then there was another murder.

The dead man was one of the witnesses at the Padgitt trial—the husband of Danny Padgitt's "girlfriend." I heard the story and then I started to carry my gun with me again.

Malcolm Vince died in the north of Ford County. It happened when he left a bar. Somebody shot him in the head. Nobody was with him at the time and there were no witnesses. The police had a lot of questions, but no answers.

I wrote the story for the *Times*, but I didn't put it on the front page. Most people in Clanton read the story, and some were afraid. The Padgitt name started to come into conversations again.

Christmas came and went. The Ruffin children all visited Miss Callie and Esau, and I went to Memphis. I had Christmas dinner with my grandmother and then I drove back to Clanton. Everything there was quiet and the same as always.

January was cold and boring. There were no new stories in town. I was in my office one day. I started to write about the life of an old man from Clanton. It was a difficult job because it wasn't a very interesting story.

Suddenly, I heard the sound of a gun—and the window in my office broke. Glass flew across the room. I quickly got down on the floor, under my desk.

There were more shots—two, three, four—but they didn't hit the *Times* office. I put my hand up on the desk and found the phone. Then I called Harry Rex.

"Where are the shots coming from?" I asked him.

"There's somebody on top of the courthouse," he said. "The Sheriff's there now with some policemen. Stay in your office, Willie."

"I'm not going anywhere," I said. "I can get the story later."

There were eight shots, then it was quiet. I moved a little closer to the window, behind a chair. There were more shots, then nothing for a minute or two. I looked out the window at the courthouse.

On top of the building I could see the man with the gun. His hair was white and there were thick black lines across his face. *He's crazy,* I thought. The police were down in the street, behind cars. Some ran across to the courthouse. Two of Sheriff Coley's men started to shoot at the gunman.

Everything was quiet for a time. We waited for about twenty minutes before the police brought a man out of the building. It was Hank Hooten.

Two days later, Hank Hooten went to a **mental hospital**. The police learned a little from his doctors. Hank didn't really want to kill anybody. He was angry because Danny Padgitt didn't get the death penalty.

The story was on the front page of the *Times*, and we sold a lot of newspapers that week.

mental hospital /ˈmentl ˌhɑspɪtl/ (n) You go to a *mental hospital* for help with problems in your head.

CHAPTER 4

In Jail, but Free

*I followed the car into town. They went into the
City Café and had lunch. I took photos.*

One day in the summer of 1977, a woman walked into my office. I knew her face, but I couldn't remember why.

"I'm Darla Clabo," she said. "I worked in the courthouse in 1971. I was there when Danny Padgitt was on trial."

She left Clanton some time after the trial and moved to Alabama. She was in Clanton again now because she had a story for me.

"I visited my mother in Broomfield last week," she said. This was a small town about three hours' drive from Clanton. "In the afternoon, I went for a walk in town and saw a man in a café. I remembered that face. Another man was with him, but I didn't know him. The two of them looked very friendly. When the first man said something, the other man laughed. But I didn't go into the café because I was afraid."

"Why?" I asked.

"The first man was Danny Padgitt."

"But he's in Parchman Jail. I don't understand …"

"The other man wore a white shirt with the words 'Broomfield Jail' on it," Darla told me. "One of my friends works at the jail, so I asked him about Danny Padgitt. Padgitt moved to Broomfield from Parchman in 1974."

"But why was he in town?" I asked. "Why wasn't he in jail?"

"I don't know, Mr. Traynor. But this isn't right. I want you to go there, and I want you to write the story for the *Times*."

I drove to Broomfield and waited outside the jail with my camera. At 11:30 A.M. a car drove out of the jail. Inside it were Danny Padgitt and another man. I followed the car into town. They went into the City Café and had lunch. I stayed outside and took photos.

Later, I talked to the waitress in the café.

"They come here three times a week," she said. "They eat chicken or hamburgers and Danny always pays."

I went back to Clanton and wrote my story. The front page of the *Times* had two large photos of Danny Padgitt on it. One was in the City Café. The other photo showed the two men in the street in Bloomfield, with big smiles on their faces.

People in Clanton were very angry. Why wasn't Danny Padgitt in jail?

Why was he in town? Why did he look as free as his jailer? They wanted answers.

"The Padgitts' money is going to Broomfield Jail," said Harry Rex. "Danny can go into town because they're paying the jailers."

Miss Callie saw the photos in the newspaper and she felt afraid.

"She didn't sleep last night," Esau told me.

The next day, I had two phone calls. One was at home and one was at the office. The man said the same words each time:

"You're dead."

I told the Sheriff. After that, there was a police car outside my house each night. Every morning, it followed me to work. Then it stayed in front of the *Times* office all day.

I put the gun in the car again and I was very careful. But nothing happened.

Some time later, after stories in other, bigger newspapers, Danny Padgitt moved back to Parchman Jail. There were no more trips to town for him.

◆

There were eighty-eight churches in Ford County. Sometimes I visited one of them and then I wrote about the church in the *Times*. I wanted to visit all eighty-eight. I went to churches for black people. I went to churches for white people. Some were big, some were small. They were all different.

One Sunday I went to a little church in the north of the county. The people weren't very friendly so I sat at the back. At the end, everybody stood up and walked past me to the door. I didn't know these people, but then I looked at one man more closely. I remembered his face from many years before. He was very thin and he looked older and grayer, but it was the same man. It was Hank Hooten. Why wasn't he in the mental hospital?

I looked for him outside the church. There were a lot of people there, but I couldn't see Hank Hooten. Maybe he saw me and left quickly.

For two days after that, I tried to find him. I phoned the hospital, but they didn't tell me anything. I asked people in the small town near the church. But I was a stranger there and nobody wanted to speak to me.

3.1 Were you right?

Think about your answers to Activity 2.4. Then answer these questions.

1 Who shot at the windows of Willie's office?

....

2 What did Willie do?

....

3 Where was the man with the gun?

....

4 Why did he look strange?

....

5 Why was he angry?

....

6 What happened to him after the shooting?

....

3.2 What more did you learn?

Finish the sentences with words from the box.

mother	café	write	afraid
worked		understand	trial

This is Darla Clabo. She [1]..................................

in the courthouse in 1971. She remembers the

Padgitt [2]... .

One day, six years later, she visited her [3] .... in

Broomfield. There, she saw two men in a [4]... .

She was [5]... because one of the men was Danny

Padgitt. She doesn't [6]... why he was in the town. She

wants Willie to [7]... the story for the *Times*.

3.3 Language in use

Read the sentences in the box. Then finish the sentences. Use these words:

> I quickly got down on the floor, **under** my desk.
>
> The police were down in the street, **behind** cars.

below	into	above	outside	between	in	next to

1 Willie was .... his office when glass flew ....
   the room.
2 Hank Hooten was on the top of the courthouse, ...
   the street.
3 The police car was .... Willie's window.
4 Hank came out of the courthouse, ... two policemen.
5 Danny sat in a car .... a man from Broomfield Jail.
6 Willie stayed .... the café and took photos.

3.4 What happens next?

Read the sentences in *italics* at the top of page 22. Then look at the pictures in Chapter 5. What do you think is going to happen next? Why? Make notes.

Notes

Room 25

"He's going to come out, Willie. This year, next year …"
"But somebody has to fight it."

One of my college friends also worked for a newspaper. It was a big, important newspaper in Memphis. Late one Sunday night in 1979, my friend phoned me at home.

"Are you going to the **parole** hearing tomorrow?" he asked.

I was tired and it was late. I didn't understand.

"What parole hearing?" I asked.

"Danny Padgitt's," he said. "Tomorrow, ten o'clock, at Parchman Jail."

"I didn't know about that!"

"They don't tell anybody. I heard about it this evening. It's your story and I wanted to tell you," he said.

Early next morning, I spoke to Harry Rex.

"Most people in jail are black and have no money," he said. "They don't ask for parole because they know nothing about it. But the Padgitts have Lucien Wilbanks and they have money."

Next, I phoned the Sheriff. He didn't know about the parole hearing.

"And I have to go to Memphis today," he said. "I can't change that now—it's too late."

"Padgitt went to jail in 1971—that's only eight years," I told him. "Will he really be free tomorrow? I have to stop this."

At eight o'clock, I jumped in my car and drove out of Clanton. Two hours later, I was outside Parchman. I ran into the jail.

"Where's the parole hearing?" I asked somebody.

"Up the stairs, Room 25," he said.

---

parole /pəˈrəʊl/ (n) People can sometimes get out of jail early. They or their lawyers have to ask for *parole*. At a **parole hearing**, lawyers and other people discuss the question and say yes or no.

I looked at my watch. It was a minute after ten o'clock. I ran up the stairs. A policeman stood outside Room 25.

"I'm here for the parole hearing," I said.

Then I pulled the door open, and I walked in.

Everybody in the room turned and looked at me. Lucien Wilbanks was there with the Padgitt family. Danny Padgitt was there with a jailer. There were also five men at a table by the window.

"Who are you?" one of the men asked me.

"He's from the newspaper!" shouted Lucien Wilbanks angrily.

"Which newspaper?"

"The *Ford County Times*," I said.

"This parole hearing is not open to everybody," said the man at the center of the table. "You can't come in."

"Who can be here?" I asked.

"Mr. Padgitt's family and lawyer, and people from the Kassellaw family," he said. "Not newspaper people."

"And the Sheriff?" I asked. "Can he be here?"

"Yes, he can."

"But nobody told him about it," I said. "So I'm here from Ford County for the Kassellaw family. I'm going to speak for them."

The parole hearing started. Lucien Wilbanks spoke. Danny Padgitt's mother spoke about her son. Then Danny spoke.

"I'm a better man now," he said. "I learned from my mistakes. I do a lot of good work in this jail. And I'm studying …"

I listened to all of this. Then I had to speak.

"I'll tell you about the murder," I said. "And I'll tell you about the trial." And I did. There was one more thing before I finished. "At the end of the trial, Mr. Padgitt turned and spoke to the jurors," I said. "He said, 'I'll find you and I'll kill all of you.'"

The five men looked at Danny Padgitt.

"Did you say that?" one of them asked him. Danny didn't say anything. "Did he say it?" the man asked Lucien Wilbanks.

Wilbanks started to speak, but I quickly stood up. I spoke first.

"Ask the people at the courthouse in Clanton," I said. "They wrote everything down."

"Sit down, Mr. Traynor," said the jailer.

"I can send you the notes," I said. "You can't give this man parole—

it's not right."

The five men left the room. We waited for half an hour. When they came back, Danny Padgitt had to stand. We all listened. Two of the men wanted to give him parole, but three didn't. So Danny Padgitt stayed in jail.

When I drove home I felt very tired, but happy. I went to my office and wrote the story. It was on the front page of the *Times* that week.

◆

My next church visit was the week after the parole hearing. On Sunday morning, I drove out of Clanton and found the church. It was almost full of people. There was a man there in a **wheelchair**. I knew his face. It was Lenny Fargarson, one of the jurors.

"Will Danny Padgitt get out of jail?" he asked me.

"Yes, he will," I said. "But I don't know when. He can ask for parole every year. One day, he'll be free."

"Do you think he'll come back to Ford County?"

"I don't know. Maybe. The Padgitt family are all here."

"Will you call me when he's out of jail?" Lenny asked.

Lenny's parents were also at the church. Mrs. Fargarson invited me to lunch with them at their house. They were kind people and I was hungry. It was a nice idea. At lunch, we talked for a long time. Some of

wheelchair /ˈwiːltʃer/ (n) People use a *wheelchair* when they can't walk.

our conversation was about Danny Padgitt.

"I'm not afraid," said Lenny. "God will look after me."

But his parents were afraid. I could see that.

◆

A year later, Danny Padgitt asked for another parole hearing. I wanted to go.

"Why?" asked Harry Rex.

"We stopped it last time," I said.

"He's going to come out, Willie. This year, next year …"

"But somebody has to fight it."

"You'll make the Padgitts very angry. And you know that they're dangerous. Nobody in Clanton will want to go to the parole hearing with you," Harry Rex said.

He was right. But this time, the parole people at Parchman told the Sheriff about the hearing, so the two of us went.

The same men were there. They remembered me. The Sheriff went into Room 25 at Parchman Jail, but I couldn't go in.

The policeman at the door took me back to my car. I had to sit there and wait. I couldn't do anything. But I didn't have to wait very long.

"This time, four said yes and only one said no," the Sheriff told me. "So Padgitt's free."

I wrote a very angry story for the *Times*. I put it on the front page and everybody talked about it. The people of Clanton weren't happy, but they couldn't do anything about it.

Sam Ruffin was home and the Ruffins invited me for dinner. Sam and I talked in their yard before we ate. Sam was unhappy about Danny Padgitt's parole, too.

"Mom can't sleep," he said. "She thinks about this all the time, and she isn't eating much. The doctor came yesterday. We all have to look after her. Is Padgitt really back in Ford County now?"

"I think he's with his family. He has to stay in the state. But we don't see any of the Padgitts in town. They never come into Clanton."

"Do you think there'll be any problems with him?"

"No, not really."

"Please tell my mother that. She won't listen to me," Sam said.

"Is she afraid?" I asked.

"Yes," said Sam. "I think she is."

"Padgitt won't come into Clanton," I said. "It will be OK."

"But you remember his words at the end of the trial."

"They were only words, Sam. He was afraid and angry," I said. "Nothing will happen. In a month or two we'll all forget about him."

But I didn't feel as happy as I sounded.

4.1 Were you right?

Look back at your answers to Activity 3.4. Then circle the right word in each sentence below.

1 Danny has *two / three* parole hearings at Parchman Jail.

2 Willie speaks at the *first / second* parole hearing.

3 The Sheriff goes to the *first / second* parole hearing.

4 Willie thinks that Danny is staying near *Memphis / Clanton*.

5 *Everybody / Nobody* knows where Danny is.

6 Miss Callie is *happy / unhappy* about Danny's parole.

4.2 What more did you learn?

Who says what? Write the letters next to the sentences.

1 "I'm a better man now." ☐

2 "He's going to come out, Willie." ☐

3 "I do a lot of good work in this jail." ☐

4 "Will you call me when he's out of jail?" ☐

5 "Nobody in Clanton will want to go to the parole hearing with you." ☐

6 "God will look after me." ☐

4.3 Language in use

Read the sentences in the box. Which of these words can go in each sentence below? Write one word, or more than one.

> It was very dark **because** there were no windows.
>
> 'I don't want to lose you, **so** I'll do this.'

after	because	before	so	when

1 Willie only heard about the first parole hearing .... a friend called him.

2 The Sheriff couldn't go to Parchman .... he had to go to Memphis.

3 Willie wants Danny to stay in jail, ... he goes to the parole hearings.

4 .... Danny speaks at the first hearing, Willie tells the five men about the end of the trial.

5 .... Danny is a free man again, Willie writes an angry story for the *Times*.

6 Sam Ruffin talks to Willie about his mother's problems .... Willie eats with the family.

4.4 What happens next?

Discuss the pictures in Chapters 6 and 7 with other students. What can you see? What do you think is going to happen? Then read these sentences and write *Yes* or *No*.

1 Lenny Fargarson dies. ....

2 Another juror dies. ....

3 Somebody shoots Miss Callie. ....

4 The Sheriff arrests Danny. ....

CHAPTER 6

A Juror Dies

Nobody could kill Miss Callie in her house in Lowtown.
There were too many people there.

"Fargarson is dead," said Harry Rex on the telephone. "This is the start, Willie."

"What? How?"

"Somebody shot him in the head."

"Where was he?" I asked.

"At the front of the house, in his wheelchair. The police are there now."

Lenny Fargarson's mother was out at the stores. She found him when she came home. There was a lot of blood, so Mrs. Fargarson didn't move anything. She called the police first, then her husband at his place of work.

I drove to the Fargarson house. The Sheriff was there, and a lot of policemen. Some friends and family were also there. I didn't see Lenny's parents. The young man was on the ground, dead, next to his wheelchair and an open book.

I looked away from the house. There were trees around the yard.

"The killer shot him from those trees," the Sheriff said. "You can't see anyone in there."

"Why Lenny Fargarson?" I asked him.

"He was easier than the other jurors," said the Sheriff. "He couldn't run. Willie, I want the other names—now. Do you have them?"

"Yes, in the office. I can meet you in an hour. What's your plan?"

"We have to tell those people."

I went back to my car. There were policemen everywhere, outside the Fargarson house and in the trees.

When I took the names of the jurors to the Sheriff's office, he looked at them carefully. One man was dead, so he sent policemen out to the homes of the other ten jurors.

"You don't have to go to Miss Callie," I said. "I'll tell her."

I went to the Ruffin house that evening.

"Miss Callie, something very bad happened this afternoon," I said. "Lenny Fargarson is dead. Somebody shot him."

Miss Callie was very sad, and she was afraid, too. She remembered Lenny very well.

"He was a nice boy," she said. "I liked him."

After that she was very quiet. We sat outside the house—Esau, Sam, Miss Callie, and me. Esau went into the house and made tea for us. When he came out again, he had his gun. He put it under his chair. Miss Callie didn't see it, but Sam and I did.

The houses in Lowtown were very close. We could see people next door and across the street. Some families were in their front yards. Six or seven young boys played a game in the street. They laughed and shouted. Nobody could kill Miss Callie in her house in Lowtown. There were too many people there.

"She's OK here," I said quietly to Sam.

I went back across Clanton. There were a lot of policemen outside the jail. I thought about the first murder. I remembered Danny Padgitt's face when they brought him in, and the blood on his shirt.

The Sheriff was in his office.

"Two of the jurors left Ford County last year," he said. "We're looking for them. And we can't find Danny Padgitt. He has to stay in the state—but where is he? His family isn't saying."

The next evening, I visited the Ruffin family again. It was a hot night and we sat outside the house. There was a police car at the end of the street. Across the road I could see two of the neighbors. They had guns with them.

"They're watching," said Sam. "Day and night."

Back in the center of Clanton, there was nobody in the streets. Everybody in town waited, but it was worse for the jurors and their families. They were all afraid.

CHAPTER 7

Who's Next?

"It was the same gun," the Sheriff said. "It's the same killer, Willie.
He's a dangerous man and there are nine more jurors."

Mo Teale worked for farms everywhere in Ford County. On June 15th a farmer in the north of the county phoned Mo's company. There was a problem with one of his machines.

Mo and another man drove to the farm. The machine was a long way from the farm house. The two men drove near it. Then they stopped their car and walked. They found the problem and Mo worked on the machine for a minute or two. His friend went back to their car for something.

There was a sudden noise and Mo Teale fell to the ground, dead. His friend heard the gunshot, but he didn't see the killer.

Mo and his workers wore yellow shirts, so the gunman could see him easily. I remembered his yellow shirt because I saw it every day at Danny Padgitt's trial. Mo was another of the jurors.

The Sheriff called me to his office.

"It was the same gun," the Sheriff said. "It's the same killer, Willie. He's a dangerous man and there are nine more jurors."

"Can't you stop this? Can't you arrest Danny Padgitt?" I asked.

"I have a police car outside the house of every juror," said the Sheriff. "And I have four cars near the Padgitt house. But we don't know that it was him. There weren't any witnesses."

I found Harry Rex in his office.

"Let's go for a drive," he said.

We drove around Clanton. We went past a small house in a road near the town center. At the front of the house were a lot of cars. One of them was a police car. Every light in the house was on.

"Maxine Root's home," said Harry Rex. "She sat at the front, next to Miss Callie."

I remembered Mrs. Root. Now her front yard was busy with friends and neighbors. Some of them had guns. We drove past slowly and everybody watched us.

Then we drove to the north of Clanton. In a wide street near the woods we found Mr. Earl Youry's house. I couldn't remember him.

"He sat at the back," Harry Rex said. "He always wore a brown jacket and a white shirt."

There were cars in front of Mr. Youry's house. Many of his neighbors sat on chairs in the front yard, with guns. A police car was also there. Harry Rex stopped next to it. He knew the policeman.

"Are those people there all the time?" Harry Rex asked.

"All day and all night," the policeman said. "Nobody can get close to Mr. Youry. He's OK."

It was the same in Lowtown, outside the Ruffin house. Miss Callie's neighbors were there, at the front and back doors.

"People will stay here all night," Sam told us.

Harry Rex drove us back to my house. We sat in the yard and talked about the killings. We talked about Danny Padgitt.

"He planned these murders very well," I said. "They're different from Rhoda's murder. There was no plan there. Who do you think will be next?"

We didn't know.

"He'll wait," said Harry Rex. "Maybe for a long time. In a month or two, people will start to forget. The neighbors will get bored. The police will have to do other things. He'll try again then."

I wanted to talk to Harry Rex about something different.

"I had a visitor in the office yesterday," I told him. "Somebody wants to buy the newspaper, for a lot of money."

"Do you really want to sell the *Times*?" he asked.

"I'm thinking about it. Maybe it's a good idea. What do you think?"

Harry Rex thought about it.

"What will you do? Where will you go?" he asked.

"I'd like to take a trip to Europe—maybe to India, too. I'm thirty-two years old, Harry Rex. I want to see some of the world outside Ford County. With the money from the *Times*, I can do that."

"It won't be the same without you, Willie," he said. "Will you come back to Clanton?"

"Yes, this is my home," I said. "But it's only an idea for now."

Harry Rex was quiet. Then he drove home.

I went to bed and thought about Miss Callie and the other jurors. I couldn't sleep. I thought about my idea, too. Europe … India … It was an exciting plan.

5.1 Were you right?

1 Look back at your answers to Activity 4.4. Then look at these pictures. Why are these important to the story? Talk to other students.

2 Now put these words in the sentences.

neighbors   policemen   jurors   gunman

a Two of the .... are dead.

b The same .... shot them.

c Miss Callie's .... are watching her house.

d There are .... outside every juror's house.

5.2 What more did you learn?

Put these sentences in the right order, 1–8.

a ( ) Willie tells Miss Callie about Lenny Fargarson.

b ( ) Mo Teale dies.

c ( ) Miss Callie's neighbors watch her house.

d ( ) Lenny Fargarson dies.

e ( ) Willie talks about a possible new life.

f ( ) Willie and Harry Rex drive past the Root and Youry homes.

g ( ) The Sheriff asks Willie for the jurors' names.

h ( ) Mrs. Fargarson calls the police.

5.3 Language in use

Read the sentences in the box. Then make sentences with *could* or *couldn't*.

> The gunman **could** see him easily.
>
> I **couldn't** remember him.

1 Lenny .... run from the gunman.
2 The policemen .... see anybody in the trees.
3 From Miss Callie's house, Willie .... see people next door.
4 Nobody .... find Danny Padgitt.
5 The Sheriff .... arrest Danny.
6 Willie went to bed, but he .... sleep.

5.4 What happens next?

Look at the name of Chapter 8 and the sentences in *italics* below it. What do you think will happen to these people now?

A Miss Callie ....
....

B Maxine Root ....
....

C Earl Youry ....
....

D Danny Padgitt ....
....

Miss Callie Remembers

"Mr. Padgitt was guilty—we all knew that. But only nine jurors
wanted the death penalty. Here are the other three names."

Two other newspapers were interested in the murders of Lenny Fargarson and Mo Teale. I had a phone call from the Memphis newspaper and then from one in Jackson. I told them the stories.

But I was bored now with my job. I could sell the *Times*, and this was a more interesting idea to me now. I wanted to go away. I sat in my office and thought about it some more. Then there was a phone call for me. It was Sam Ruffin.

"You have to come here," he said. "Mom wants to talk to you."

The same neighbors were at the Ruffins' front door. Sam met me in the street and took me into the house. Miss Callie was in the kitchen. She looked very tired and unwell.

"In here," she said.

We followed her into the bedroom and she closed the door. There were some papers on the bed.

"There's something wrong," she said. "I don't understand it. We jurors couldn't remember everything at trial. People said a lot of things. So we made notes and looked at them again later. These are mine." She showed us the papers.

"At the end, we went into a room and talked about the trial. Nobody outside that room heard our conversation, of course. And every juror said, 'We will never tell.' But this is too important. I can't stay quiet."

Miss Callie looked through the papers.

"Here it is," she said. "Mr. Padgitt was guilty—we all knew that. But only nine jurors wanted the death penalty. Here are the other three names."

Miss Callie showed us the page. On the left, there were nine names.

On the right, there were three: Lenny Fargarson, Mo Teale, and Maxine Root.

"You see the problem," she said. "Why did these two jurors die?"

"He's killing the wrong people," said Sam.

"But Danny Padgitt didn't know the names," I said.

"No, but …" Miss Callie stood up and took the paper from my hand.

"I have to tell the Sheriff about this," I said.

"No, we all said … You can't tell him the names …"

"Mom, this is important. For Maxine Root, most of all," Sam told her.

Miss Callie put the papers back on the bed.

Then there was the sound of people in the kitchen. Bobby and two of his brothers were here. Miss Callie went out to the kitchen. She suddenly looked happy again.

Sam gave me his mother's papers.

"Take them to the Sheriff," he said.

The Sheriff wasn't in his office, so I visited Harry Rex. I showed him the names.

"Maybe these three took money from the Padgitts. Maybe Danny is starting with them because he doesn't want them to talk. Then he'll kill the other jurors."

"Not Lenny Fargarson," I said. "He didn't take any money. I know that."

"So what do you think?"

"Maybe Lenny was the first because he was easy. He couldn't get out of his wheelchair. Maybe Mo Teale was next because he was out in the country, away from people. So he was also easy."

"And who'll be next?" asked Harry Rex.

"I don't know. I have to take this to the Sheriff now," I said.

I stood up and walked to the door.

"One more thing, Willie," said Harry Rex. "Sell the *Times*. Go away and have a good time. But don't leave Clanton."

I smiled at him. "OK, I won't."

The Sheriff was on the phone.

After a minute, he said goodbye and put the phone down.

"That was Earl Youry," he said. "He remembers something, and it's very strange. The three jurors …"

"I know," I said. "I spoke to Miss Callie this morning."

"Did she tell you the names of all three jurors? Mr. Youry can't remember the woman's name."

"It was Maxine Root," I said.

The Sheriff phoned Maxine. I heard her crying at the other end of the phone.

"I can't arrest him, Maxine," the Sheriff said. "But we'll look after you. There will be policemen with you at work, and at your house. They'll be there all the time."

The Sheriff put the phone down and he thought for a minute.

"I'd like to talk to Lucien Wilbanks," he said. "Maybe Harry Rex will come, too. But Lucien won't want you there, Willie."

This wasn't a problem. Harry Rex told me the story later, but I couldn't put it in the newspaper.

"I talked to Danny and his father," Lucien told the Sheriff and Harry Rex. "He's not the killer. He was in the Padgitt office on those days. There are witnesses."

"How many of these witnesses have the name Padgitt?" asked the Sheriff.

"I can't give you any names," Lucien said. "But they're good witnesses."

"One more murder and Clanton will go crazy," said the Sheriff. "Then I'll have to arrest Danny. Tell him that."

"He's not the killer," said Lucien. "And I'm telling you the truth."

◆

Two weeks later, the mailman carried a box to Maxine Root's house. It was big and it was heavy. Next to Mrs. Root's address was the name of a famous Californian candy company. On the back of the box was the name of the sender. It was Mrs. Root's sister, Jane.

The policeman at the front of Maxine's house took the box into the kitchen. Maxine was afraid of Danny Padgitt. She was also bored because she had to stay in her house most of the time. So she was very happy when the candy arrived from her sister. She started to open the box, then stopped. She wanted to thank her sister first, so she went to the phone.

Maxine and her sister talked about different things—the weather and Jane's children.

"Thank you for the candy," Maxine said then.

"What candy?" said Jane. "I didn't send you any candy."

After Maxine finished her phone call, she looked at the box again. Yes, Jane's name was on the back. She moved the box. It was very heavy for candy.

There were three policemen outside the kitchen window. Maxine called to them.

"Please look at this box of candy," she asked them.

They walked around it and turned it over.

"OK," said Travis, the oldest of the men. "Stand back, everybody. I think this is dangerous."

He put the box in the yard and walked back into the kitchen. Maxine and the other policemen stood behind him. Then he opened the window and took out his gun.

"You're going to shoot my candy?" asked Maxine.

"This isn't candy, Mrs. Root."

"Let's call the Sheriff first," one of the other policemen said.

"No, I can do this," Travis answered.

He shot at the box, but he didn't hit it. He tried again and this time he hit the box.

There was a very loud noise. The windows broke and glass flew into the house. The glass hit Maxine and the policemen. The back door fell onto the floor inside the kitchen.

The glass cut the other two policemen and Maxine very badly, but Travis lost his right arm.

I heard the noise in my office across town. Everybody in Clanton heard it. When a lot of police cars drove out of town, fast, I followed them. The police closed the roads near Maxine's house. I couldn't get past, so I drove to the hospital. I knew a young doctor there.

"Nobody died," he said. "But a woman and three policemen are here. One of the policemen is very sick."

I phoned the Ruffins from the hospital.

"There was an accident at Maxine Root's house," I said.

But it wasn't an accident. I knew that. Somebody wanted to kill Maxine. And we all had the same idea: that somebody was Danny Padgitt.

CHAPTER 9

Back in the Courthouse

*When the Sheriff brought Danny Padgitt into the courtroom the next day,
the room was full. Everybody in Clanton wanted to be there.*

People in Clanton were very angry and afraid. The Sheriff had to do
something, but first he phoned Lucien Wilbanks.

"I have to bring Danny into jail now," he said.

"I can't stop you," said Lucien.

The Sheriff sent four police cars to the Padgitt house. When they
arrived, Danny Padgitt was outside with Lucien Wilbanks. There was no
fight. The Sheriff arrested Padgitt and they drove back into Clanton.

There were a lot of people outside the jail. When they saw Danny
Padgitt, they shouted angrily. Then the Sheriff put Padgitt in jail and
everybody went home. That night, Clanton was a happier place.

I visited Miss Callie. Her family was with her. She gave me a very
happy smile.

A party started at the house next to the Ruffins. There was music and dancing.

"Everything's OK now," Bobby said.

◆

When the police brought Danny Padgitt into the courtroom the next day, the room was full. Everybody in Clanton wanted to be there. Miss Callie arrived early and found a good place at the front. Esau, Bobby, and Sam were with her. Maxine Root's family were also near the front. They looked very angry. Maxine wasn't there—she was in the hospital. I saw Mr. and Mrs. Fargarson at the back of the courtroom. There were no Padgitts.

"They're not here," said Harry Rex. "It's dangerous for them. People are very angry."

A door opened and the lawyers came in. We all waited quietly, but we didn't have to wait long.

There was a sudden loud noise above us. A gunshot. Women started to cry and somebody shouted, "Get down!"

I looked at Danny Padgitt. The **bullet** hit him in the arm and he fell back. The gunman shot a second time. This bullet hit Danny in the head. He didn't move again.

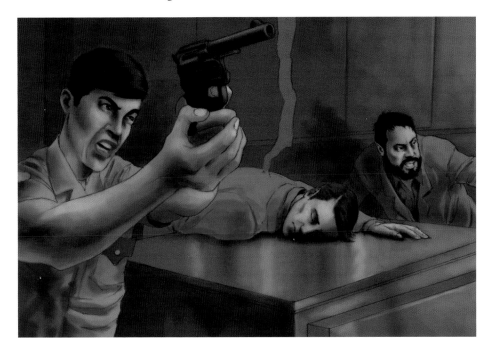

Most people ran outside, but I stayed with the police. They looked up. Above the courtroom was a small room. One window looked onto the street, but the other looked down into the courtroom. The gunman was up there. Policemen ran to the stairs. There were more shots from above us, but they were outside the courtroom now. I went to a window and looked out. Outside, people looked up, then ran away. There were more shots: one, two, three. Each shot broke a window across the street from the courthouse. This was Lucien Wilbanks' office. Four, five, six windows. The gunman broke every one.

bullet /ˈbʊlɪt/ (n) When you shoot with a gun, a *bullet* comes out.

6.1 Were you right?

Look back at your answers to Activity 5.4. Then look at the pictures in Chapters 8 and 9 and check (✓) the right answers below.

1 Miss Callie shows her notes to Willie and Sam.

   a She doesn't understand and wants their help.

   b She wants Willie to take the notes to the Sheriff.

2 Somebody sends Maxine a box.

   a It is a box of candy from her sister.

   b Her sister doesn't know anything about the box.

3 The Sheriff arrests Danny Padgitt.

   a The people of Clanton are very happy.

   b The jurors are afraid of the other Padgitts.

4 Next day, Danny Paditt is taken into the courtroom.

   a Danny says that he is not guilty.

   b Danny dies before he can say anything.

6.2 What more did you learn?

Circle the right word or words in each sentence. Then talk to another student. Who or what are these people talking about?

1 The jurors said, "We will *have to / never* tell."

2 Sam says, "He's killing the *wrong / right* people."

3 Willie says, "I *have to / can't* take this to the Sheriff now."

4 The Sheriff says, "Mr. Youry *can / can't* remember the woman's name."

5 Maxine says, "Please *look / shoot* at this box of candy."

6 Harry Rex says, "They're not here. It's *dangerous / difficult* for them."

6.3 Language in use

Read the sentences in the box.
Then finish each sentence below
with a comparative adjective.

> This was a **more interesting** idea to me now.
>
> That night, Clanton was a **happier** place.

1 Miss Callie looked .... every day.
(unwell)
2 Miss Callie looked .... every day. (sick)
3 The box of candy was .... than Maxine
thought. (heavy)
4 The policemen were .... of the box than
Maxine. (afraid)
5 The courtroom was .... for Danny's
hearing in the courtroom than for his first trial. (busy)
6 It was a .... courtroom this time. (full)

6.4 What happens next?

1 **Who is the gunman? What do you think?.**

   a Who shot Danny Padgitt? Why?

   ....

   because ....

   b Did the same person shoot Lenny Fargarson and Mo Teale? Why did
   they die?

   ....

   ....

2 **Look at the picture on page 54. Discuss these questions.**

   a What is Willie doing? Why?
   b Who will be unhappy about this? Why?
   c What will Willie do in the future, do you think?

CHAPTER 10

The Killing Stops

"People in Clanton have to know the truth," I said.
"He killed people in the town."

After about an hour, the shooting stopped. For some minutes there was no sound from above us. But the gunman had one more bullet. He put the gun to his head. Down in the courtroom, we heard that last shot.

A policeman ran down the stairs.

"It's OK now!" he shouted. "He's dead! And it's Hank Hooten!"

Most people didn't remember Hank Hooten.

"Who's he?" they asked.

"That crazy lawyer," somebody said. "He went to the mental hospital in Whitfield."

Slowly, the last people in the building started to leave the courthouse. Miss Callie wasn't well, so the Ruffin family took her to the doctor.

I went back to my office and made a phone call. Then I drove out of Clanton.

I waited for a long time in Whitfield Mental Hospital. Outside Dr. Vero's office, I read magazines and drank coffee. He was a very busy man and he didn't want to see me.

"I'm not going away," I told the girl in the office. "I'll wait here all day, and again tomorrow."

After more than an hour, the doctor came out to me.

"Mr. Traynor, I told you on the phone. I can't talk to you about Hank Hooten," he said. "I was his doctor. I can't tell you anything."

"People in Clanton have to know the truth," I said. "He killed people in the town. Their families are asking a lot of questions and they want answers. Why wasn't Hank Hooten in a mental hospital? How sick was he when he left here?"

Dr. Vero thought about this for a minute or two.

"I'll talk to you," he said. "But you can't put *everything* in your newspaper."

"I understand," I said.

"OK. Let's go for a walk."

We left the hospital offices and walked across the yard outside. We found some chairs and sat in the sun. Then Dr. Vero told me Hank Hooten's story.

"When he came to this hospital in January 1971, he was very sick. His mother was sick, too, before she died, and possibly his grandmother. We often see these problems in families. Mr. Hooten talked a lot about Rhoda Kassellaw. He wasn't good with women. I don't think she was interested in him. But he was in love with her and he was very angry about her murder. After she died, he heard her in his head. She asked for his help—she wanted Danny Padgitt to die. So Mr. Hooten wanted the death penalty for Rhoda's killer, but three jurors didn't. Mr. Hooten learned their names. I don't know how. And he hated those jurors.

"In 1976, Mr. Hooten left Whitfield Hospital. His doctor sent him home."

"But why?" I asked. "He was a very sick man, so why didn't he stay here?"

Dr. Vero didn't know. "I had a job in Chicago at that time," he said. "I came back to Whitfield in 1978, after Hank Hooten left. I can't tell you more than that, Mr. Traynor. That's the truth. Sometimes doctors think that people will be better at home. And, of course, mental hospitals never have much money."

"You knew Hank Hooten," I said. "What do you think? Was his doctor right when he sent Hank away from here?"

"I can't answer that, Mr.Traynor. You know that."

"Thank you for your help," I said.

"Will you send me your story before you put it in your newspaper?"

"I will."

I drove into the town of Whitfield and stopped the car. Then I walked up the street to a café and thought about Hank Hooten and Clanton.

How did life there get so crazy? It was a small American town, the same as hundreds of other towns. Then, one night, Danny Padgitt killed Rhoda Kassellaw. After that, everything changed.

I thought, too, about *my* life in Clanton. I didn't want small town life now. I wanted to see the world. *Now—I'm ready now*, I thought.

I asked for a hamburger and coffee. Suddenly, I was very hungry.

There was a telephone in the café, and I phoned Harry Rex.

"Willie, you have to come home," he said. "Quickly."

"Why?"

"Callie Ruffin's in the hospital."

"How bad is she?" I asked.

"She's very bad."

I didn't eat the hamburger. I paid the waitress and left the café. Then I drove back to Clanton as fast as I could.

I found Esau and the eight Ruffin children at the hospital.

"She's sleeping now," Bobby told me.

"What does the doctor say?" I asked.

"It's not good," said Sam. "But they're trying."

I couldn't see Miss Callie, but I waited at the hospital with the Ruffins.

Two hours later, we saw the doctor again.

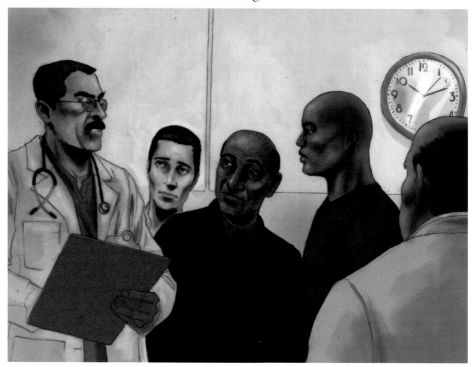

"She's asleep now," he said. "You can't do anything here, so go home. Get some sleep."

Sam took Esau back to Lowtown. But it was a very small house, so the other Ruffin children came with me. There were more bedrooms in my house.

We all went to bed, but we didn't sleep.

The next morning, I had to go to my office. The new editor of the *Times* wanted to start work that week. I started to put my books and papers into boxes. But every time I looked at something, I remembered a story. It was a slow and difficult job.

I went to the hospital in the afternoon, but I couldn't see Miss Callie. I waited in a family room with some of the Ruffin children. Suddenly, Sam ran in.

"She's worse!" he said. "The doctor's with her!"

I called Esau at Lowtown, and very quickly he arrived with the other children. It was early evening before we saw the doctor.

"I'm sorry," he said. "We can't do anything more. You can say goodbye to her now."

The family wanted me to stay with them. We stood around her bed and we cried. At about midnight, Miss Callie died.

I went back to my office and sat there. I looked out the window. The street below was dark and quiet. Across the road, the courtroom was also dark. I felt very sad.

In the morning, Bobby Ruffin phoned me.

"Are you OK?" he asked.

"I'm leaving Clanton," I told him. "I'm going to see the world. I wanted to tell her, but I waited. And now …"

"Will you come back here?" he asked.

"Yes. But it won't be the same without her. I wanted to show her my photos. I wanted to talk to her about different places. I wanted to buy her something from every country. Now I can't tell her anything."

"You know that she loved you," said Bobby. "You're one of the family. Come back here and tell us about those places."

That afternoon, I sat at my desk and took out my pen. For a long time I looked at the paper. Then I wrote my last story for the *Times*— my most difficult story:

Miss Callie Ruffin, died July 5th, 1980. A wonderful wife, mother, and friend …

1 Work with another student. Talk about Maxine Root's story on television.

| Student A | You work for the television station. Ask Maxine questions. Start like this: "On this week's *It's My Story*, we say hello to Maxine Root ..." |

| Student B | You are Maxine. Answer the questions. Remember, you were in the hospital some of the time. How did you learn about the end of the story? |

2 Work with three other students and have a conversation. Each of you is one of the people in the pictures. Danny Padgitt killed one person. Hank Hooten killed three people and tried to kill another person. Which killer was worse? Why?

You are the new editor of the *Ford County Times*. One year after the end of this story, you write about life in Clanton. First, think about these questions:

1. How is life in Clanton different now?
2. Do the Padgitts come into town? Do people in Clanton talk to them?
3. Is Lucien Wilbanks in town? Is Willie back in town? Where is Hank Hooten?

of them had guns. Then we neighbors sat in the front yard,

Clanton – a year after the killings *by*.....................

I talk to a lot of people in Clanton. They tell me that life here ....

....
....
....
....
....
....
....
....
....
....
....
....
....
....
....

Willie goes on a long trip because he wants a change from life in Clanton.

1 Read this advertisement from a magazine. You and three or four other students work for *Your Way*. What do you do each day?

LONG VACATION?
WORK VACATION?

Your Way can help with your trip. Who are you? What do you want? How many people are going? Tell us and we will plan everything for you.

You don't like to fly? No problem! You can go across the Atlantic by ship.

You don't like hot weather? Try Russia or Canada in winter.

We plan. You go. It's Your Way! Call us now

2 You are all going to plan a trip around the world for some *Your Way* customers. Talk about these questions and make notes.

  a How many people are going on the trip? How old are the oldest and youngest people?

  b Are they friends, family, or strangers?

  c What are they interested in? (Music, movies, birds ...)

Notes